HARRY
COCQUE

That's Reet Boy!

Harry Cocque is a very old Dorset gentleman, currently residing in the Piddlewell Moorhen Rest Home for the faintly bewildered (but non-violent).

Harry was born in 1920. He loves Jaffa Cakes and corduroy trousers.

HARRY
COCQUE

That's Reet Boy!

Ludicrous tales of Dorset village life in the 1930s

Colin Baines

Matador
5 Weir Road
Kibworth Beauchamp
Leicester LE8 0LQ, UK
Tel: (+44) 116 279 2299
Fax: (+44) 116 279 2277
Email: books@troubador.co.uk
Web: www.troubador.co.uk/matador

ISBN 978 1848767 737

British Library Cataloguing in Publication Data.
A catalogue record for this book is available from the British Library.

Typeset in 11pt Book Antiqua by Troubador Publishing Ltd, Leicester, UK

Matador is an imprint of Troubador Publishing Ltd

Printed and bound by TJ International, Padstow, Cornwall, UK

For Bizzle, Looby, Lewo, Bert and Beak

INTRODUCTION

My name is Harry Cocque, and I was lucky enough to be born in the beautiful county of Dorset in the reign of the Sailor King, George V. I never saw him other than in the newspapers and on stamps, but I heard he was a pretty good bloke. Actually, I think I saw him on a plate too. Or it might have been a tea towel. Anyways, he had a fine beard and liked shooting things, so he was all right by me. One of my favourite memories is of the day of his Silver Jubilee when I was fifteen and we had quite a time on the Village Green, but there's more about that later on.

I suppose I've had a fairly eventful life, but I never thought about writing it down until I met a pleasant and stocky young fellow who reckoned people would be interested in how things used to be in the old days. He's been visiting me at the rest home, bringing me bags of soft jellies, and getting me to recall stories about the funny little place where I grew up. I've tried my best to get the details right, but I do get a bit confused these days. Not as confused as poor old Mrs Myrtle down the hall though. Whenever she sees something orange she goes to put her coat on, and she walks to the window several times a day and says, 'They're under the hedge again' before going back to her jigsaw puzzle. She's been working on that puzzle for nearly two years now and we're all desperate to know what the picture is. I think it's a beaver.

I do hope you enjoy reading this book, and if your name happens to be Jerome Punnet and you once needed a tin of talcum powder in a hurry, you still owe me half a crown.

THE FIRST CARNIVAL

Someone asked me whether carnivals happened when I was a nipper. Oh my goodness, yes they did! In fact, as I recall I was present at the very first carnival ever held in the county, when I was ten. It was between the wars in 1930, and of course you didn't smile too much in those days, in case they thought you were a spudshover.

Me and Tommy Nobkin had spent most of the afternoon picking redlumps (raspberries to you clever people) from the nuns' allotments behind the bushes next to the goose pond. Tommy was an unlucky boy; he'd lost one of his ears in a ferreting accident and had to have his spectacles tied to his head with one of his mother's old stockings. Mind you, that never stopped him going on to make the stool that the Prince of Wales fell over, but that's another story.

Anyways, me and Tommy had just finished 'topping up the pond' as we called it, when we heard a dinging sound in the distance. Well, I heard it first to be fair, Tommy was facing the wrong way. We ran down Lumpy Lane towards the sound and were surprised to see Bessie Goodbust holding a bit of bent shiny metal on a string. She was striking it with a nail and it produced such a lovely sound that me and Tommy were soon in tears with delight.

She marched off towards the village and we marched behind her. Of course we didn't have any fancy musical instruments like Bessie, so I slapped the back of my head as I marched and Tommy made an odd hooting noise.

By the time we passed the church, we had a huge crowd of people behind us. There must have been more than twelve I reckon. Even Old Albert from the ditch joined in, although he'd forgotten to put his breeches on again and got shouted at. Some folk said that Old Albert had once killed a man after an argument over a drawing of the moon. All I know is that he smelled awful and made tiny statues out of goat business and spit, which he placed in a line by the village pump every other Tuesday.

We all marched as far as the gibbet at the crossroads, where we stopped. Most people wandered off, but greasy Mr Guffer asked Bessie if she'd like to help him collect a few sticks for his aunt and they headed into the thicket. Me and Tommy followed a little way behind because we knew his horrible aunt had died months ago. We could hear Bessie giggling and climbed a tree to see what was going on. Guffer seemed to be fumbling for something in Bessie's dress, and we thought it was very funny because she always kept her sweets in her pinny.

We decided to head home as we were hungry and Tommy said it was faggot night at his house.

Everyone enjoyed the march so much that they decided to do it again the next year. Tommy had a drum by then, which was left behind by one of the soldiers that used to visit his mother of an evening. I had a brightly coloured piece of rag on a stick, and Bessie had a new baby.

OLD ALBERT

No-one knew where Old Albert came from; he just appeared at the back door of the butcher's shop one morning and asked if he could have a pig's ear to chew. He never had a proper job, but he did help out here and there and was very good at unblocking things. He had quite a collection of sticks, hooks and long rubber gloves. And some very rude postcards.

I don't think he was actually as old as he looked. I know he was once spotted trying to peer under the door of the nuns' wash house and when they gave chase he easily beat them across the field until his belt gave way, his breeches fell down and he went sprawling among the groblies. He took a fair old pummelling that day, but it didn't bother him.

Some folks reckoned he'd once been a proper gentleman because he had more than one hat, but me and Tommy had seen him throw a full milk churn over a wall so we were always nice to him. We took him an apple pie once but he just stamped on it. He said a meal wasn't a meal unless something had died. We took pasties after that.

A HARVEST TO FORGET

It must have been the long hours the labourers spent in the fields, and the way they swilled down scrumpo like it was water that made them do odd things. Judson Phatt was the labourer I remember best. He was a big strapping lad with an anvil-shaped head and a huge birthmark shaped like a winged maggot on his back. He never wore a shirt whatever the weather, and walked with a limp ever since he'd blown off part of his foot after using a loaded shotgun as a crutch in an amateur production of *Treasure Island*.

Judson had spent the whole evening in The Twitching Pig, a dingy and dirty Inn frequented by layabouts, bitter old men with pipes and anyone who had little money and no sense of smell. By throwing-out time he was roaring drunk and full of mischief. He broke into the storeroom of the ironmongers shop, stole some turpentine and headed up the hill to Widow Minger's farm. Having cornered half a dozen woolers, he threw turps on them and set them alight. The commotion brought out half the village, including me and my mate Tommy, who had been up a tree opposite Lily Titman's bedroom window.

After the woolers were finally chased down and put out, Judson was found fast asleep behind the War

Memorial. He was made to work off the damage he'd caused; he had to repaint the ironmonger's soffits and Widow Minger had him up at her farm every night for a month. He also had to carry all the produce into the church for the big harvest festival display on his own.

The service itself was a bit special that year. The church was packed, and Reverend Toucher had surpassed himself with a wonderful sermon on how Moses would have enjoyed boiled parsnips and probably had a glass eye. After the harvest hymn, the Reverend asked the winner of the 'Guess the Weight of the Biggest Sausage' competition to collect the prize, which was a large corn dolly with a cut-out photograph of the King for a face.

Big Mrs Doodle from the bakery was the lucky one, and she hauled herself out of her pew and waddled slowly down the aisle to the front. She bent to pick up the dolly and let out the loudest bumparp I have heard from that day to this. It echoed round the altar and bounced off the ancient stone walls for what seemed like an eternity. There was then a moment of perfect silence, before Old Albert spat out his false teeth and howled with laughter.

The whole congregation collapsed into a helpless mass of merriment, until the Reverend screamed from the pulpit, 'GOD DOESN'T FIND FARTING FUNNY!' This did absolutely nothing to help, and me and Tommy took advantage of the pandemonium to cram our pockets with eggs from one of the display baskets, most of the contents of the collection plate and a mirkin we found on the floor.

Poor Mrs Doodle was too embarrassed to ever go to church again. She spent her Sundays sobbing behind the counter in the bakery, flicking raisins about and marking the sign of the cross on the window with flour. The Reverend had to save her soul by partaking of her enormous baps twice a week.

SCHOOL DAYS

School was a lot different when I was a lad. Children of all ages were put in together as there weren't enough local youngsters to make more than one class. I can recall a number of occasions when I was the only one there and even the teacher hadn't turned up. On those days I'd call out the register to myself, write things on the blackboard and give myself lines if I felt I wasn't paying enough attention.

Back then it was far more important to help at the Mill or at one of the farms, and most parents considered schooling a waste of time. They said if you could swing a scythe you didn't need to know what the Chinese ate or how tall the Eiffel Tower was, and that even Mickey the Bug could make a living.

Mickey was a worker at the Flour Mill who couldn't read, write or speak properly but turned up every day, rain or shine. He had big bulging eyes and always wore the same red smock. Mickey's job was sit next to the emergency handle and to pull it if there was an accident. He sat there day in day out for over ten years but sadly, on the day that Casper Brown got his hand caught in one of the drive belts, Mickey got confused and pushed it by mistake. This made the machinery go faster, and cost Casper three fingers and part of his nose. Mickey went a bit funny afterwards and took to pulling it every couple of hours. He was eventually sacked, and to save paying a replacement the Mill owner simply removed the handle.

Anyways, I was telling you about school. The building was old, damp and draughty and there were very few books. We had to use that shiny toilet paper to write on and we all hated the teacher. His name was Mr Viper and he didn't enjoy his job, other than handing out punishments. Tommy seemed to come in for it quite a bit as he liked to chatter, and was often made to stand on a chair at the front holding the 'talking turnip' and grizzling.

Every week Viper would tell us about the schoolmaster who had flogged a boy to death, saying that he'd love to deal with us urchins like that. This was harsh as we weren't naughty until he arrived at the school and started shouting when we spoke without raising our hands or simply got things wrong. The previous teacher, dear old Mrs Corset, had let us make as much noise as we liked as she was stone deaf. She had spent her time in class knitting endless cardigans, with the balls of wool cleverly balanced on her hump.

Viper had a sixth sense when it came to sniffing out our attempts to play tricks on him. He never sat on the drawing pins; he kicked the door open so the bucket of pigswill fell on Charlie Nettle's head and knocked him out; he wouldn't eat the spotted dick made with rabbit turds and he somehow avoided the trip wire across his garden path so the postman took the cowpat in the face instead.

I vowed to get him back when I was older, but the Germans beat me to it. I felt a bit cheated in a way, but as Tommy's grandma used to say, 'There's many a swollen acorn that never touched a cow.' I still have no idea what that means.

DIFFICULT TIMES

There were countless accidents when I was young, I don't think anyone ever thought about trying to do things safely. We lost four thatched roofs one bonfire night, when one of the farmhands built his own rockets but made the sticks too short, Alfie Smith blew himself up whilst trying to distil his own brandy, and Mr Drab was stung to death by his bees when he forgot to button the flap of his long-johns.

There were so many farming calamities I couldn't begin to tell you about them all, but we just accepted it as part of life. Widow Minger's threshing machine had seen off so many labourers it was known as The Reaper, which was a bit confusing to some. Judson Phatt painted sinister symbols in bright red on its side to represent all the limbs it had pulled off or mangled. It was eventually decided that Vernon Minger shouldn't be in charge of it any more. Mind you, he was only six years old.

We all smoked in those days too, even us youngsters. I recall one old chap kept a duck's foot in his baccy tin, to give his smoke a bit of a kick. We all thought it was good for us, as Mr Cole the tobacconist told us so. His elderly mother must have been on six or seven packs of cigarettes a day, and even when her hacking cough got so bad that she couldn't speak any more he insisted that a couple of good strong cigars would put her right. She lived to be 105.

We made our own fun back then, and you'd probably be surprised at how many happy hours can be spent with some bent wire and a broken flowerpot. Me and Tommy once went fishing at the same place seventeen days in a row without catching anything and we weren't bored. But I'll admit it was a lot more interesting after someone told us about bait.

We didn't have many places to go in the evenings either, so we had to endure years of Mr Rubus and his slide shows in the Village Hall. He didn't have many slides and all of them were of places he'd never visited, so he couldn't tell us anything about them. Attendance at his shows dwindled, until one autumn night in 1931 it was just him and old Mrs Hobson, who was blind.

TROUBLE WITH TINKERS

We first realised there were tinkers in the area when two of the geese disappeared from the pond and the allotments were stripped of the largest carrots, much to the nuns' annoyance.

The tinkers weren't Romanys. Me and my mate Tommy loved it when the Romanys came. They had beautiful caravans and if we brought them useful items like coins and petroleum jelly, they gave us chunks of roasted hedgepigs and other unidentifiable animals. They once told our fortunes and whilst I didn't believe for a moment that I would ever build a railway on Mars, Tommy was absolutely convinced he was going to marry Queen Victoria. I tried to explain that she was long dead, but Tommy stuck his finger in his ear and stomped off unamused.

The two tinkers were camped out in a small tent by the river near the place where the villagers had once erected a Rhubarb Man. It was supposed to have been a Wicker Man, but no-one knew what wicker actually was. One of the tinkers, Angus, had a thick accent so we all assumed he was French. He had been to the village some years before and had won a bet by extracting a splinter from Old Albert's left buttock with his hands tied behind his back, but that's another story.

Angus and his companion Hamish made a few pence by sharpening knives, fixing gates and suchlike, so Reverend Toucher decided they'd be the ideal men to repair the church roof. He agreed a price with them and the following morning the tinkers could be seen carrying sacks up and down a long ladder which had been lashed to the side of the church. This went on for several days, until the Reverend took it upon himself to climb up and see how they were getting on.

Tommy and I were playing squittle in the graveyard when there was an almighty shouting from above. We looked up just in time to see what appeared to be a giant crow rise from beside the bell tower and plummet down to crash through the roof of Mrs Nettle's shed. We went to investigate, and found Reverend Toucher laid out on a mound of crushed leeks. He looked dead to us, so we thought we'd better run for help.

The first person we came across was greasy Mr Guffer, who was sat glum-faced on Bessie Goodbust's front step, having forgotten his key. He'd banged on the door to no avail, and Bessie wouldn't let him use her back entrance. We told Guffer what had happened and he managed to find Doc Grimm, who thought he was a surgeon on Nelson's flagship and insisted on carrying a brace of loaded pistols and a bone saw wherever he went. Luckily, the Reverend wasn't badly hurt but half the lead from the church roof had gone, and so had the tinkers. And the butcher's handcart. And the village's reserve cheeses.

For the next few months, whenever it rained on a Sunday the choirboys got drenched and Silas Nimrod, the Verger, insisted on towelling them all down at the end of the service. Silas objected to almost every suggestion about how the church could raise money for proper roof repairs, which always seemed a bit queer to me.

THE VILLAGE SHOP

Now that I come to think about it, we did seem to make more than our fair share of mistakes and have a lot of odd people in our village. Take the time when me and Tommy were digging by the riverbank to make a dam. We dug up a clay pot full of rough coins and thought we were rich, but when we tried to spend them on treacle pop and radish fizzers in the Village Shop, miserable Mabel Warlock wouldn't take them. She told us they were Roman and no good any more, so we chucked the lot back in the hole along with a load of flattened yellow jewellery that was with them.

Mabel didn't like youngsters in her shop and would send us straight out unless we could show her that we had money to spend. She kept all the best sweets behind the counter so we couldn't pocket them, and would cram chocolate into her mouth whenever we went in just to show us that she could take whatever she liked. Sometimes we organised ourselves into relays so she'd keep doing it. She was the size of a heifer with beady little eyes and at least four chins. They had to dismantle half the shop front when she skidded on a rogue gobstopper and broke her leg.

Mabel's husband was far too lazy to help serve customers. He spent all day sat out the back in a big armchair, peering out of the window and eating tinned peaches, which he fished out with a bent tea strainer as he didn't like the syrup. He had a thin pencil moustache and wore an ancient serge greatcoat whenever he went out. Bessie Goodbust said he'd flashed her so often she'd probably seen it more than Mabel had.

DOC GRIMM

You might like to know a bit more about Doc Grimm. He was quite a character, I can tell you. He arrived in the late 1920's so I believe, as a replacement for old Doc Lyle, who'd gone stark staring mad and was dragged away one rainy afternoon by PC Stodge and a couple of big lads from the Inn. I never found out what Doc Lyle actually did, but it must have been something nasty because the surgery was pulled down soon afterwards and all of his clothes and belongings were flung on a bonfire.

Doc Grimm was a skinny man with sandy hair and a big black leather bag that he carried about in a basket attached to the back of his tricycle. I was never convinced he was a proper qualified doctor as the certificates on his wall looked suspiciously like his own handwriting, which was small and spidery, and never used the letter f.

Since there was no surgery in the village, he performed most of his doctoring in the back room of his house. It had a whole wall of shelves full of medicines and potions, an old camp bed with a curtain round it, a small desk and an enamel sink in the corner. There was always a faint metallic smell in there. If you went to see him you had to sit in his kitchen to wait, and the only way you could tell if he was in or not was to look for his cycle clips hung over a horseshoe nail that had been hammered into the wall by the door.

He loved to play golf and kept a couple of clubs by his desk. Tommy's sister told me that whenever she was getting dressed after an examination, she could hear him having a quick whack outside.

The Doc was a dab hand at stitching, which came in very handy, and he was one of the most sensible and articulate men you could ever wish to meet until he started testing the medicines on himself. He took pills and powders, rubbed on ointments and drank all kinds of strange mixtures. From then on, you never knew what to expect from him. He went through phases of dressing as a miner, a Greek god and a heron before settling on a naval surgeon. He acquired an ancient musket which he called 'Brownie', and used it to put holes in the weathervane on the church tower. The weathervane was in the shape of an angry hare and was a recent replacement after the old one had fallen down in a brisk wind and missed the Marrow Man by no more than a lark's whatsit. The Reverend was not best pleased.

He may have been unpredictable, unbalanced and a bit of a drunk, but Doc Grimm was well liked throughout the area. This was because he had come up with miracle cures for some of the locals. Mrs Jilkes had been hiccupping for eight months before the Doc stopped them dead when he kicked her Jack Russell into the river. He healed Silas Nimrod's sores by smearing them with a poultice made from lard, iodine and owl pellets, and he even solved one of the farmhands' unusual toilet problems by cutting the bottom six inches off his string vest.

His finest hour came one evening in the Twitching Pig, when Fats Tanner nearly choked on a Dorset Knob. The Doc wandered into the bar just as Fats was turning purple and his eyes were popping in his head. Without a word, the Doc strode across the room and grabbed Fats between the legs. Fats coughed hard and the half-chewed biscuit flew out of his mouth and knocked the counters off the Seven Men's Morris board. After that, the Doc always got his first drink free, and had a special beer named after him. It was called Grimm Brew and it was the worst beer I've ever tasted.

THE STEAM FAIR

It was one drizzly lunchtime in 1932 when Tommy's mother said she'd take us to the Steam Fair if we shifted some sacks of coal round to the back of the cottage and filled all the scuttles. It took us ages as the wheelbarrow was very squeaky and rusty, and we never thought of oiling it. We'd just come back from the woods, where we'd been looking for elves. Ernie Snook had told us he'd seen one running about in a grey suit, but we couldn't find any tiny footprints or anything, and after an hour or so we returned the cage we'd borrowed from Mavis Monk and decided it had probably been a squirrel all along.

We set off for the Fair which was in a large field a couple of miles away. As soon as we got near we could hear a wonderful tune on a steam organ, and me and Tommy broke into a run, leaving Tommy's mother and his big sister Elsie to catch up. They had bickered the whole journey, as Elsie had decided to wear a red bonnet and Tommy's mother was convinced everyone would think she had no drawers on. Elsie must have been about eighteen then, and some folk said she was 'A Proper Teaser'.

We wandered around the Fair and were spellbound by the fantastic machines, the noise, the crowds and the smell, which was a mixture of steam, candy floss and unwashed bodies. Tommy's mother kindly gave us a few pence each, which we spent on a roundabout ride and three goes on the big wheel. I was hungry, so I headed straight for the rissole stand. Tommy wouldn't eat them because his grandma had told him they were made of 'Earholes, eyeholes and arseholes', so he had a bag of chive tips instead.

As the afternoon drew on, we watched several men fail miserably at one of the 'Trials of Strength', where they had to strike a peg as hard as they could with an enormous mallet, and try to ring a bell at the top of a tall board. The board was brightly painted with a grinning clown holding a measuring stick to show how weak or strong you were. Finally, a chap who looked grimy enough to be a blacksmith hit the peg with such force that the bell was knocked clean off the top and landed on the prize cart, smashing a line of chalk figurines to dust.

Just after that, we noticed that a lot of men and older lads were gathered round one of the rides and were yelling and cheering as it turned. It was the Chair-O-Plane and as we walked towards it we couldn't see what was so interesting or entertaining. Tommy's mother was frantically trying to persuade the ride operator, a swarthy little man in a flat cap, to make it stop. He just shook his head and laughed, and that's when we realised what all the fuss was about. Elsie was on one of the swings and Tommy's mother had been right about the drawers.

That was the end of the outing. Tommy's mother

marched Elsie away and me and Tommy thought we'd better call it a day too. As we were leaving, Tommy spotted a threepenny bit on the ground and picked it up. We then had a terrific idea. We'd come back the following day after the Fair had moved on, and search for all the coins that people were bound to have dropped, but as it turned out we never got the chance. We were caught trying to bunk off school and kept in late as a punishment. By the time we made it back to the field it had a bull in it.

MARROW MAN

We didn't have many places to eat out back then you know. You could get a bowl of stringy rabbit stew at The Twitching Pig if you were lucky, and sometimes the Marrow Man would visit on a Saturday afternoon if it wasn't raining. The Marrow Man had a horn with a rubber bulb that he'd honk when he was nearly at the Square, and me and my mate Tommy would run there as fast as we could, yelling, 'Marrow Man, Marrow Man, we want double!' He would yell back, 'Double is for fatty larks, pip, pip, pip!' which made us laugh like bottled stoats.

The Marrow Man was a smiley little chap with big bushy eyebrows and a top hat. He always had a ready smile and raised his hat whenever he saw a lady, so we were a bit taken aback when we heard he'd battered his wife to death with a poker when she forgot to draw a face on his boiled egg.

HUNT THE THIMBLE

Years ago, people didn't have all the things you take for granted these days. We had to get by with what we had, and if things got broken we had to fix them as best we could.

My mate Tommy's grandma was an expert at making clothes for all the poor local families from bits of rag or whatever could be found. She would sew all day long, fuelled by cups of weak gooseberry tea while singing songs that always seemed to contain some reference to illness or the loss of a loved one. She was the oldest person I knew, and she sometimes told us tales of how her policeman father had helped in the hunt for Jack the Ripper, before being stabbed by a criminal mastermind wearing a monocle. We were thrilled by these stories, and were disappointed to discover many years later that he'd actually been a rat catcher who'd spent most of his time in a Weymouth brothel with a six-foot African woman called Pixie.

Tommy's grandma made him some wonderful hats too. As he only had one ear, she neatly added loops of string to the sides of a tea cosy to hold his glasses on, and padded the top of it with newspaper to make him look taller. She once made me a scarf which brought me out in a terrible rash, so I used to hide it in the coal bunker and retrieve it when I visited. Whenever I forgot I had to endure a lecture on how stiff necks lead to baldness, and how Napoleon wore a scarf when he conquered Egypt.

Then one morning she lost her favourite wooden thimble. Despite the best efforts of Tommy, his mother and his sister Elsie, no trace of it could be found, so several of us were called in to help. We turned the whole cottage upside down, searched the garden, the shed and the outdoor privy where she spent several hours each day. We found rusty pins and half-chewed toffees, one of which still had a tooth in it, but no thimble. When I tried to be helpful and ran to borrow a metal one from Lily Titman, Tommy's grandma threw it back at me and told me to stick it, 'Where Adam stuck his thumb.' I didn't know anyone called Adam so I gave it back to Lily.

It finally dawned on us that she fed Old Albert's mongrel Woodrow from time to time, and that perhaps he'd swallowed it with some scraps. Tommy and I raced off to the corner of the allotments where he usually went to do his business and started poking the fresh piles with sticks. I found something hard in one of them and flicked it into the air, but it flew past Tommy leaving a streak across his shirt and plopped into the pond. We waded in and searched all afternoon, but it was a hopeless task.

When we returned at teatime cold, tired and covered in mud, we found Tommy's grandma happily sewing a patch onto someone's vest. It turned out that she had a hidden box full of thimbles and was just being awkward, the stupid old bag.

THE BARN DANCE

My mate Tommy was taken to hospital a week before the Barn Dance. One of our experiments to graft on a new ear using gramophone parts, horse hair and a darning needle had gone badly wrong.

The Barn Dance was one of the highlights of the year, and just about everyone from the district would come for a good drink and a fumble. This one was going to be a bumper turnout, as some of the soldiers from the nearby base had been given permission to attend. Tommy's sister Elsie spent most Friday nights at the army camp. I think she liked their rations as she often told me how she got plenty of sausage up there.

A top local band, Much Trotter and the Fetlocks, were booked to play and mad Mr Mungo was to be the caller. He had once been to prison for impersonating Boris Karloff's nanny at a tea shop in Bridport and had a withered arm.

This time someone had suggested fancy dress, and it led to some rare sights in farmer Hale's big barn, which the butcher had tastefully decorated with inflated udders. Balloons were hard to come by in those days. The butcher himself turned up wearing a hollowed-out pig's head, and was disappointed when no-one seemed to notice. Fanny Muffet was the centre of attention with her tiny nurse's outfit. Judson Phatt couldn't take his eyes off her all evening; he'd been obsessed with Fanny for years.

The evening was well under way and gallons of scrumpo and cheap ale had been consumed by the time the soldiers arrived. They had entered into the spirit of things by dressing up as soldiers, which the ladies thought was marvellous. The dancing had degenerated into a bit of a free for all, as mad Mr Mungo had long since passed out in a puddle of his own vomit. Maid Marion was dancing with the Kaiser, and a nun had lifted her habit and was high-kicking her way around the barn supported by a slightly grubby jester. Whether or not it was a real nun was anyone's guess, but I'd have thought a genuine nun would have worn bloomers.

Anyways, all was very enjoyable until one of the soldiers tried to lead Fanny Muffet outside. This was too much for Judson, who stepped into his way. The soldier took a wild swing which Judson easily ducked, and Doc Grimm, who was in full naval uniform and blind drunk, took the punch full in the face. It would have knocked his teeth out if he'd had any. Instead he collapsed to the floor, discharging both of his pistols and his bladder in the process. The first shot whined away harmlessly, but the second took Silas Nimrod in the chest. As luck would have it he'd come as a medieval knight and his selection of oversized saucepans and guttering saved his life. A brawl ensued between the labourers and the soldiers, which was only stopped when farmer Hale fired both barrels of his shotgun into the air, bringing down part of the roof and several dead bats.

I watched it all from behind the sprout-on-a-stick stand with a few of the other youngsters, and it was the best entertainment we'd had since Old Albert disgraced himself at the Sunday School picnic. He shouldn't have eaten all those Bile Beans.

COMIC BOOKS

Me and Tommy loved comic books, although we could hardly ever afford to buy any. We used to get them after Ernie Snook had finished with them, which was as soon as they were creased or a new one came out. My favourite was *The Whooper*, which featured my hero, Sir Simeon Spiker. He was fabulously rich with lots of glamorous girlfriends, yet still went on adventures all over the world. He was ace at everything and each week he would do something amazing. He would rescue a team of shapely nurses from a burning hospital, land a crippled aeroplane when the pilot was blown up by a bomb, massacre a whole tribe of natives with a Maxim gun when they attacked a British fort, shoot tigers, pandas and crocodiles to make coats and bags for a princess, or lead an uprising against a brutal Oriental overlord who'd be hacked to bits by the mob.

The best episode was when he strangled a spy in a snow-bound castle, hijacked a night train across Europe, slit the throat of a secret policeman disguised as a porter, hitched a ride on a steamer and fought off pirates, yet still made it back to Wembley in time to score the winner in the FA Cup Final. He then sank eleven pints of beer and three bottles of Champagne before driving his sports car at breakneck speed back to his huge house, cooking a surprise breakfast for his valet and taking a well-deserved shot of cocaine.

I can't understand why they don't make comics like that any more.

THE SALESMAN

The day the salesman arrived in his shiny grey motor car, everyone in the village swarmed around it. Cars were a rare sight back then. I think it was 1933, the same year the maypole collapsed after someone told Tubby Thorne there was spare key to the bacon store stuck on the top and the dope tried to climb it. Tubby didn't live in the village, but would turn up from time to time to see if he could scrounge something to eat. We used to chant, 'He loves his pork, and his friend is a fork. He loves his meat, but he can't see his feet.' He'd scowl at us and threaten us with a beating, but we'd just run away laughing.

Anyways, I can't remember what make of car the salesman had now, but it may have been an Austin Flob, or possibly a Morris Gimp.

The man that stepped out of it was tall and slim with a full red beard. This caused a certain amount of murmuring, as most villagers believed that people with red hair came from Ireland or Sweden and were common thieves and vagabonds. He spoke politely to Mrs Doodle, who had pushed her way to the front of the onlookers, and asked who he should see about hiring the Village Hall. He then strode off to find Silas Nimrod, pausing only to whip out a large handkerchief and wipe the dirty finger marks, saliva and nose prints from his windscreen.

Me and Tommy trailed after the stranger as we didn't have much else to do. We'd been playing football with Ernie, but there were only the three of us and it was a bit one-sided. We'd wandered off, much to Ernie's disgust, and left him to play with himself. Ernie was a stroppy boy whose family had more money than the rest of us. They lived in a big house with their own telephone and had clean clothes every single day. I was never allowed beyond the front door, but I do remember Ernie's big sister Eileen letting us look down her knickers in the back garden once.

Anyways, the man from the car asked us to put up some posters about a grand sale that was to take place after Old Soldiers Club had finished. We tacked up a few, but used most of them to make boats which we floated down the river and chased until Tommy tripped and hurt his knee. As a result of our laziness, there was a pretty feeble turnout when the half-dozen slow-witted and limbless locals, none of whom had ever been anywhere near the army, packed up their shove ha'penny board, finished saluting each other and dragged themselves off home.

The salesman had a couple of trestle tables with all sorts of domestic appliances on them, but hadn't realised that the National Grid had only just reached us. Most people were either scared stiff of electricity or too poor to buy anything that ran on it. He did sell a wireless, which were all the rage as everyone loved listening to *Mrs Duff's Magnificent Mangle*, and the butcher's wife bought an electric kettle which she melted on her range the next morning.

When he returned to his car, he discovered that someone had scrawled 'Go home Redface' on the roof with a big lump of chalk, then found he couldn't start it despite cranking the handle hundreds of times. This may have been because Old Albert had packed the exhaust pipe with dirt, but no-one thought to mention it at the time. After a while, Judson Phatt volunteered to tow it to the main road and fetched one of farmer Hale's carthorses. As he was backing it up, the horse lifted its tail and dropped several pounds of steaming hot dung in a big heap on the bonnet, and as the car was pulled slowly away with the hapless salesman inside, the younger village children gestured at him and threw rotten vegetables.

So far as I know he never returned, although I don't know why. He got a far better reception than the man from the District Council, who was carted out of the village and tied to a bus stop with his braces and laces. They left him there with his briefcase jammed on his head and his official papers screwed up and stuffed down his trousers. Someone stole his bowler hat and it was used for making blancmange for years afterwards.

NEWSPAPERS

I was one of the few folk in the village that could read well, and since I was always interested in what was going on in the world, I liked to read the newspaper as often as I could. The problem was that the only person in the district who had them delivered every day was the local Baron, who owned half the district and was as mean as a buzzard. As luck would have it, Lily Titman got a job up at the Manor House as a chambermaid and as well as telling us tales of all the goings on amongst the servants and the Baron's peculiar family, Lily very kindly sneaked out one of the newspapers for me every day. I think it was the *Daily Trump*.

There weren't all that many photographs in the papers back then, but there were lots of advertisements for marvellous things we could never afford, and a very funny cartoon strip called *Pipples and the Squeezer*. Pipples looked a bit like a startled cat in a boiler suit, but could walk and talk and had a magic lathe. The Squeezer was a baby with enormous hands.

It was in the newspaper that I first read about *King Kong*, which was the first 'H' film I ever saw. Me and Tommy were only thirteen, but they weren't so bothered about your age in those days. We had to spend Tommy's birthday money to get in, got ticked off by a grumpy old man for putting our feet on the back of the seats in front, and the film frightened the clods out of us. We missed the bus and had to walk home, and Tommy got stung by a hornet. I've never liked monkeys from that day to this.

In that same year, I remember they published a picture of the Loch Ness monster that made quite a few of the locals fearful of going anywhere near the Baron's lake. I knew that from time to time there were horrible things that floated there, but that was usually when we were out on an adventure and Charlie Nettle couldn't wait until he got home.

If it were a fine evening, I would often sit with the paper on the bench under the only street lamp, which was on one side of the Village Square. I'd wait until old Mr Farley came to light it with his long pole, then I'd read titbits to him, Old Albert, Mr Faff and anyone else that happened by. I'm sorry to say that I'd sometimes make up stories just to see the looks on their faces. I once told them that a volcano had erupted in Manchester, but their only concern was for the Ice Cream Man, as that was where his delivery three-wheeler had come from. I never made up anything about Herr Hitler though, who was appearing more and more often, but when I showed them photos of him they were convinced it was Charlie Chaplin in a decent coat.

Not one of the newspapers ever went to waste. On Mondays I dropped it off at the Village Hall, where there was a weekly class for making miniature papier mache sugar bowls, and on Wednesdays Silas Nimrod would come and collect it as he said he liked to check on his investments. The Wednesday edition always had the ladies' fashion pages and the 'Gusset of the Week' competition, and although I've got no proof I reckon he won it several times. All the rest ended up cut into squares and hung on a string in Tommy's mother's outhouse. Whenever Tommy headed out there, his grandma would yell at him, 'Just the three! Just the three!' This was because she said you only needed, 'One up, one down and one to polish'.

THE VILLAGE CHURCH

It might seem unusual to some of you people nowadays, but when I used to go to church as a young man I had no idea what denomination it was. No-one in the village was entirely sure as we never received any visits from bishops or the like. We took it that it was probably Church of England as it had a Cross of St George flag flying above the bell tower.

Before Reverend Toucher arrived, we had a minister or vicar, or priest or something, who was simply known as Brother Edward. He was quite seriously disturbed and had upset just about everyone at one time or another, mostly through suddenly running up and shrieking at them or by poking them in the ribs with the handle of a large wooden spoon he always carried. He died suddenly one summer afternoon in the middle of a baptism ceremony at the river. He grabbed his chest, fell face forward in the water and floated slowly away. The rest of the worshippers hid his spoon under a rock and sidled off home.

A few days later, some of the more senior villagers broke into the church and found some peculiar things; the big bible in the pulpit had had the middle removed and contained a half bottle of whisky, several empty pillboxes and a loaded revolver; the parish record books were mostly blank apart from a few pages which contained crude sketches of animals; all the robes in the vestry cupboard had gone, and in their place was a fireman's helmet and a suspender belt. There were also several well-thumbed copies of *Ooh Sir!* laying around in the office, which mysteriously disappeared.

The elders decided they needed someone with a little more discretion and travelled to Wimborne to see if they could poach a replacement. By chance, they found Reverend Toucher fuming by the side of the road, having failed an interview at St Almoth's by insisting that Noah's Ark was probably an early type of Zeppelin. He was offered the position of vicar for our village on the spot.

Reverend Toucher was an instant success. The church was cleaned for the first time in decades, the organ was repaired and a cunning new system for the singing of hymns was devised. The Reverend knew that the majority of his congregation didn't understand hymn numbers, so he spent ages marking all the hymn books with leaves. All he then had to do at the service was hold up the relevant leaf and everyone could find the right page. He'd forgotten that very few people could read either, but the thought was there.

He conducted christenings and funerals with great dignity, even when on one occasion a suspiciously heavy casket was dropped at the altar and two bodies rolled out, as the undertaker had tried to sneak in a free one. The undertaker was put in the stocks which were still by the main entrance, and had all manner of foul things rubbed in his face.

Do you know, I never saw any of the nuns in church. Maybe they just didn't like it.

FAMILIES

A lot of people ask me whether folks were different when I was a lad, and I suppose they were. To start with, families were much closer then. Tommy's cousin Jimmy had all sorts of problems as his mother was also his aunt, and rumour had it that she was his sister too. In fact we tended to call all women over the age of about 30 'Auntie', just in case.

Of course it was difficult to know ladies' ages back then, because so many of them were pug-ugly and quite a few wore wigs. Years of working lengthy hours outside in all weathers, no makeup and centuries of inbreeding had produced some hideous creatures. Fanny Muffet's sister Madge had such a long face that she looked like a mare about to foal, and Mr Guffer told us that was why she'd been ridden by most of the labourers. We laughed along with him, although we didn't understand what he meant at the time. When I asked Madge if I could have a ride a few days later, she said she'd meet me behind the Old Barn that night. I wasn't sure it would be much fun riding around in the dark so I didn't go.

A BIG BANG

There was an unusual sight for Farmer Hale one spring morning in 1934, when he was out walking his dogs in the lower pastures. Someone had abandoned a traction engine in the entrance to one of his fields, right against the five bar gate. This had happened a couple of times before somewhere up near Shaftesbury so I heard, something to do with road tax and the new motor lorries that had started to appear. He headed back to his farm to ask some of his workers to shift it.

Farmer Hale's farm was the largest in the area and he employed a lot of the locals in one way or another. He was a hard-working man who always looked as though he needed a shave, and had a liking for itchy jackets and collie dogs. After she caught him with two of the stable girls and a selection of leather harnesses, his wife refused to live with him in the farmhouse. She slept in the cowshed, in a kind of shelter made out of corrugated tin and old barrels. Their son Dale and daughter Gail tried many a time to get her to go back, but she was having none of it. Instead, she spent her days making flapjacks and sent Gail into the village once a week to sell them. The flapjacks weren't all that pleasant to be honest, as they had a whiff of dung about them, but Gail had such beautiful big blue eyes we all bought them anyway.

Widow Minger had the neighbouring smallholding, and I think she was a bit jealous of the way Farmer Hale made money. She'd been pretty well-off herself when she was young, until her husband sold most of their land on the quiet and sneaked away with her sister to start a new life in America. Sadly for him, he chose to leave on the *Titanic*. She set her cap at Farmer Hale for a while, but when he showed no interest she turned her attention to Dale. We all knew she was wasting her time, as Dale wasn't like most of the other young men at the time. He knew how to iron clothes, could cook and sew, helped Gail with her hair and cried when any of the farm animals went off to slaughter. Widow Minger could have been the prettiest woman in Wessex and it wouldn't have made any difference. If all she wanted was a new man around the place, she should have tried Doc Grimm. He'd have been there like a rat up a drainpipe.

I nearly forgot I was telling you about the traction engine. A couple of labourers went to sort things out and tried to push it out of the way, but it was far too heavy for a pair of idiots like them. They decided to light a fire in it and drive it back to the farm, and they sat in the sun, smoking and telling jokes, until the engine started to make a hissing noise a bit like a kettle. Neither of them had a clue how it actually worked, so they started pulling levers, turning wheels and unscrewing things, while the noise grew louder and louder. Luckily, they'd given up and had just started to wander off down the lane when the boiler exploded. They were both blown over the hedge and into the next field, where half a dozen pigs had dropped dead from fright.

The explosion was so powerful Old Albert said it had rattled his false teeth, and Silsas Nimrod, who'd been grooming his spring onions, watched sadly as his lean-to collapsed onto his water butt. Mrs Nettle was so convinced it was an earthquake that she spent the next two days under her dining table, and would only eat toast.

Most of what was left of it was carted off by the Rag and Bone Man, but small pieces were found all over the place and I think two of the wheels were used to make tables in the Mill's canteen. The biggest bits were dragged back to the farm and stowed behind the bean hofflers. They're probably still there.

Three or four weeks later, a couple of chaps from up north came to the village in a little maroon van and told a group of us stood by the Green that a friend of theirs had been taken ill while delivering a traction engine. He'd told them he thought he'd left it somewhere around these parts and they'd come to collect it. We said we didn't know anything about it but wished them luck with their search. They thanked us and were about to drive away when Ernie Snook opened his big mouth and started to tell them what had really happened. Charlie grabbed him and threw him to the ground, while I just stood and stared at them and Tommy started screaming and hitting himself in the face. They left in quite a hurry.

THE HAUNTED BRIDGE

Did I tell you about the time that Tommy spent a couple of days wandering past girls with a large spud down the back of his pants? He thought it would make them laugh, but they just groaned or jeered at him. All of them apart from little Amy Stodge, who started crying and ran to tell her father, who was the village policeman. We never usually saw much of him as he spent most of his time with his pal Bingo Burford propping up the back bar of The Ploughman's Neck, which was named after a local farmhand who'd been hanged for taunting the Mayor of Blandford's favourite pig, but that's another story.

Nobody in the village liked Bingo Burford. I can't remember why he was called Bingo, but he was involved in a lot of gambling and shady dealings. He was a big sweaty man with a hook nose and a false thumb made out of a clothes peg. He claimed to have lost his thumb to leprosy when he was a boy, but Tommy's grandma said he'd dropped a crate of Gentleman's Relish on it. He was eventually taken away after a break-in at the Manor House when the massive silver tea service was stolen. I heard he was caught handling the Baroness's jugs.

Anyways, PC Stodge could often be seen weaving

his drunken way home on his bicycle quite late of an evening and Tommy wanted to pay him back for the clip round the ear he'd received for the spud incident. A clip round the ear was no joke for Tommy, and he was madder than a skinned rat.

We decided to give him a scare by dressing up as ghouls and jumping out when he rode over the bridge by the standing stone. For costumes, we'd joined together a number of flour sacks and we'd practised a number of different ghoul noises till we'd settled on one we liked. We got our chance on a Friday night just as the church clock struck eleven. Spotting a lamp coming round the bend, we ran into the lane howling and waving our arms before we realised it was someone else and Stodge was twenty yards behind. Whoever was on the first bicycle screamed and swerved into the side of the bridge, flying straight over the handlebars and down into the river with an almighty splash.

Stodge jumped off his bike and raced toward the river as we just stood there. I stripped off my costume quick and threw it over the nearest hedge, then turned to Tommy who was looking down at the river. I hissed at him that I couldn't believe he'd stuck another spud down his pants at a time like this, but he hissed back that he hadn't.

Tommy scuttled away and I joined the growing number of villagers who'd heard the commotion and were helping to drag a hysterical Fanny Muffet onto the bank. Doc Grimm was trying to insist that she get out of her clothes before she caught a chill, but she was having none of it and stalked off.

For years afterwards, everyone approaching the bridge after dark would dismount from their bicycle, horse or cart in case the trolls appeared, and loads of people claimed to have seen them.

THE DONKEY RACE

For many years, our village carried on a fierce rivalry with a similar-sized village in Wiltshire. It all stemmed from an incident long ago at an agricultural show, when one of their number disagreed with the judge of a ploughing competition and threw a handful of dung at our winning farmhand. There was furious shouting and name-calling, and from that day on each village issued an annual challenge to the other to prove who was Top Hog.

The challenge was usually a cricket match, but in 1935 the pitch we used had been invaded by moles and was unplayable. All attempts to trap the moles had failed, leading some frustrated person to resort to dynamite. This certainly saw them off, but left a series of huge craters and parts of the score board embedded in nearby trees. The cricket match was duly called off.

There were a number of suggestions for an alternative, ranging from a William Tell crossbow challenge using apples balanced on the heads of children from the opposing village, to a blindfolded tadpole-eating contest. In the end, agreement was reached with a one mile donkey race over a marked course round a neutral field.

My mate Tommy was selected to be our jockey as he

was fairly weedy and lightweight. He was thrilled with the honour, and spent several days making a racing cape from an old Spanish flag he'd found wrapped around a tin leg in the ironmonger's dustbin. He also found a plaster cast of someone's bare bottom, and we were desperate to know whose it was. We wheeled it round in an old pram for several days, but no-one looked ashamed or embarrassed when they saw it. Mrs Fosse, who was a bit short-sighted, even tried to give it some milk from a baby's bottle. Tommy sold it to Silas Nimrod in the end. He got three shillings for it, but I reckon Silas would have paid a lot more.

Anyways, when the day of the race arrived it was pouring, and had been for some considerable time. Despite the dreadful weather, the turnout was huge; just about everyone from both villages assembled at the field, waiting for the competitors to arrive. Tommy turned up and received a loud cheer from our side, but sadly the Wiltshire donkey had gone lame on the journey over so couldn't take part.

After some discussion, the Wiltshire lot accepted that all Tommy had to do to win the race was to complete the course. He duly set off, waving to everyone, and slowly made his way round the field. It looked as though it was all going to be a bit of a non-event until Doc Grimm, who must have taken something powerful that morning as his eyes were the colour of fried beetles, spotted Tommy's cape and immediately assumed that he was witnessing a Spanish invasion. He called on one of the soldiers from the camp, Sergeant Longstaff, to order a counter attack before running towards Tommy, brandishing his pistols.

The driving rain ensured that the pistols wouldn't fire and as it happened, the Doc lost his footing in the mud and sprawled out in a heap at the feet of the Wiltshire crowd. They all roared with laughter, and so did we when we heard Tommy yelling and looked behind us. He had nearly made it to the end of the course when his mount, a jack, spotted the jenny from Wiltshire and did what comes naturally. Tommy held on gamely with his hair plastered to his head and a look of utter misery on his face.

Everyone present found the whole situation very comical, and in the general air of goodwill agreed that perhaps the village rivalry could now be considered a thing of the past. We all shook hands and began to go our separate ways, happy that everything was as it should be.

Then one of the Wiltshire lot threw a handful of mud at Tommy.

TIDDLEBED WINE

Lots of folk made their own wine back then you know, out of all sorts of stuff. Mrs Nettle made various kinds, but never used nettles. She said it would be like crushing her own children, which seemed a peculiar thing to say, even for someone who wore a padded helmet so she wouldn't hurt herself when she threw herself to the ground if anyone sneezed. I suppose that's why her husband disappeared on an errand to find a left-handed peeler, or it might have been because he finally had enough of her constant whining about fruit.

The most powerful concoction by far was the Tiddlebed wine made by the nuns. They sold it to make money for candles and suchlike, and Tommy got hold of a bottle when his grandma bought it, having mistaken it for pile lotion. Tommy sneaked it out of the house and drank the whole lot one afternoon in the churchyard. I don't remember why I wasn't with him that day. I might have gone for a haircut. Anyways, I found out later that Tommy eventually crawled home on his hands and knees and was thrashed for soaking his breeches, trying to eat his sister's stockings and throwing up on his grandma's slippers.

CHRISTMAS AT THE MANOR HOUSE

Just before Christmas, Lieutenant General Erasmus Ponsonby-Smythe, the local Baron, invited all the villagers to the Manor House for a celebratory meal, to reassure himself that he was in touch with the local community. He had entered the army as a captain, but his leadership had been so spectacularly inept he was rapidly promoted to a position where he could do the maximum damage from the safety of a beautiful chateau eight miles behind the lines. He was later put on trial for 'Offending public decency with midgets' which ultimately led to his election to Parliament, but that's another story.

Every villager was expected to dress in their Sunday best and take a small gift, which would be solemnly accepted by the old fool and then promptly chucked away. I was taking a bag of walnuts which I'd recently swapped for a squirrel's tail, and Tommy had some interesting gravel in a jam jar.

The celebration was held in an enormous tent on the Manor House lawn, and everyone jostled for position so they could admire Reverend Toucher. He was the only one of us who knew how to use cutlery properly and didn't blow his nose on his napkin. The Baron and his scrawny wife sat at a separate raised table a good distance away, waited on by a matching pair of sullen servants.

When we first arrived, the Baron couldn't decide whether or not he should rise for us peasants and ended up half-way in a kind of crouch. We thought we had to copy him, and whilst we remained frozen in that uncomfortable position, poor Mrs Doodle let one go. The Reverend gallantly came to the rescue by taking the initial note and humming the first verse of *Oh Come All Ye Faithful*.

The meal was served, and our table became a blur of hands, many of which had fingers missing from assorted farming and milling accidents. The mounds of food were torn to pieces and gorged within minutes, while the Baroness looked on in horror. Every last drop of wine, ale and stale lemonade was greedily quaffed and we all waited for second helpings, which never came.

The Baron delivered a long rambling speech, which no-one could hear over Old Albert's snoring, and a group of Mummers performed admirably until one of them tripped over the pole of his hobby horse. He smashed a lantern, set his costume on fire and ran screeching towards the lake, returning shortly afterwards to thunderous applause.

After some tuneless carol singing it was time to form a line and hand over our presents. As I tried to get up I found that my breeches were caught on a loose nail on my chair, so I got one of the nuns to hold my nuts while I pulled myself off.

The event ended abruptly. Mrs Nettle's generous gift

of ginger beer had fermented for too long, and the shaking it received on the trip from the village had made it dangerously unstable. The bottles started to explode and the Baron, thinking he was back in Flanders, did what came naturally to him; he ran away.

TRADITIONS

I've heard that somewhere up country they roll a cheese down a hill once a year and a load of fools chase after it. We didn't do anything quite as daft or dangerous as that, but we did have our own traditions. We had an Easter Egg Hunt which was always held in July as it was less likely to rain, and on All Hallows Eve everyone stayed indoors after eight o'clock while 'The Jabber' crept around the lanes in a hooded cloak, carrying a red lantern and a sickle. If he saw you through the window you were supposed to cross your eyes and spit twice to confuse the Devil. I still do it now.

We also had a ceremony called 'The Beating of the Meat', which took place on the seventh Friday after St Wite's day. It involved a candlelit procession from the standing stone near the bridge, to the top of Spume Hill. Everyone in the village was expected to attend, with four bearers called 'Feremen' carrying the carcass of a roasted boar on a kind of ornamental pallet. The boar had a bag of broad beans in its mouth, and wore a tiny hat made out of a crusty roll. I was a Fereman twice, once when I was selected and once when it was actually Charlie's turn, but he ran off just before the start as he said he was touching cloth. Anyways, at the end of the parade the end the boar was thrashed with sticks before being carved up and eaten with cold cabbage soup while we all stood in a circle. I once asked Reverend Toucher what on earth it all meant, but he just shrugged his shoulders and sighed. I think he was in a bad mood because that morning's 'Boil an Egg for Jesus' breakfast sing-a-long had been a complete disaster, with an even higher number of scaldings than usual.

The only other tradition I can remember was that you had to pat the village pump three times if you passed it while wearing clogs. It was something to do with the Green Man and how he'd only provide water if you thanked him for getting wood. That doesn't sound quite right, but it was along those lines. I do know that one Saturday in the Square I met Charlie and Tommy who'd just returned from a cycle trip to Sturminster Newton where they'd gone to see one of the new-fangled telephone boxes. They'd been as excited as anything until they realised that they didn't have anyone to call, so they took a whizz in it and cycled back home. They were so busy telling me about it, they walked straight past the pump and before you could say 'Jack Jubbleton' Mrs Doodle came waddling out of the bakery and straight across the Square towards us, howling and waving her pudgy arms. We all stared at her open-mouthed, until suddenly her drawers fell down round her ankles and over she went. We ran and picked her up, which wasn't easy, and helped her back to the bakery where she recovered with a cup of sweet tea, a huge macaroon and half a tin of Huntley and Palmers. In between chewing and swallowing she warned us not to forget to pat the pump in future, and we promised that we wouldn't. It was only as we walked back to Tommy's house that we realised we were all wearing boots.

RAMBLERS

We didn't get all that many visitors to the village back then, but I suppose it was a bit off the beaten track and not very well signposted. There were enough to annoy the locals though. You've probably seen films where strangers go into a pub and everyone stops talking and stares at them. It wasn't at all like that with us, as the landlords were perfectly polite. They just doubled their prices.

I remember when one couple came to the Inn on a Sunday afternoon and asked for a cream tea. Fanny Muffet looked blank for a moment, before serving them a brew in some off-white cups.

Most visitors were ramblers who trailed around the lanes and footpaths, up and down the hills, and generally got in the way. We could never work out what on earth they found so interesting, as one field looked pretty much like another to us. I did stop a man one day to ask him why he'd come, and he told me it was because the air was so much sweeter and everything was peaceful and quiet. I suggested he stay awhile, until the farmers sprayed their crops with manure and you could hear the butcher finishing off whichever poor creatures were due the knife. He was another one I never saw again.

JOLLY JUBILEE

Most folk were very patriotic back then you know. I think just about every household had a Union Flag, and quite a few had bunting tucked away for special occasions. In early 1935 the whole lot was brought out, washed and ironed, and hung up round the village. It had been announced some weeks previously that there was to be a day of celebration in honour of King George's Silver Jubilee, and we were all keen to do our bit.

The parish council had taken it upon itself to organise a whole series of events, and so far as I can recall, every last villager was involved in one way or another. My job had been to shovel all the dung from the lanes, which I didn't mind as I knew I'd get a few pence for it from an elderly couple who lived out by the edge of the woods. Their garden reeked something rotten, but their roses always looked superb.

I remember the day of the Jubilee very well indeed. It was bright and warm, and there was enough blue sky to make a happy drayman a pair of pantaloons and probably a nice pullover as well.

The first part of the jollification was a parade through the streets, led by Mr and Mrs Unwin who were dressed as the King and Queen. They hadn't been living in the village all that long, and ran a picture framing business from home. Mavis Monk, who lived next door to them, said they were very hard-working and were often banging away quite late into the night. They were chosen because Mr Unwin had a pretty decent beard and so, to be fair, did his wife. They wore yellow cardboard crowns and purple cloaks made out of the spare curtains from the church vestry.

Following Mr and Mrs Unwin were all the younger children, who were dressed in various shades of red, white and blue, and everyone clapped and cheered as they passed. There was also one soldier from the camp with them who played *God save the King* on his battered bugle. It was the only tune he knew, and by the time the parade reached the church we were fed up to the back teeth with it.

We had a short thanksgiving service in the church which was spoiled a bit as Old Albert coughed and spluttered all the way through it, until the Reverend climbed down from the pulpit and offered him a boiled sweet saying, 'For cough'. Well that's what it sounded like to me. Everyone then made a beeline to the Green for lunch.

There was a wonderful spread before us. All the trestle tables from the Village Hall were in a long row and covered with plates of egg and piccalilli sandwiches, kale chutney and bowls of brawn. There was diced swede, rabbit drumsticks and goodness knows what else. Every last morsel was eaten, and there was quite a hubbub until we were all called to order by PC Stodge pulling out his truncheon and pounding it on a table. Speeches were made by a few local dignitaries before we gathered round a radiogram that had been set up on a crate so we could listen to the King's broadcast. It was difficult to hear much of what he said because the dynamo used to power the radiogram was a bit noisy, but he got a huge hurrah when he finished.

The rest of the afternoon was supposed to have been taken up by a game of giant chess on the Green, but there were a few difficulties. The carpenter who'd spent weeks making all the pieces hadn't realised there should have been two different sides and had painted them all black. The ironmonger quickly solved this problem a bucket of whitewash and a large brush. It was then noticed that the squares marked out on the Green were only six by six so there were several pieces left over. Some young lads then took the bishops to use as goalposts for a kick-about, and the extra pawns were whisked away by Mrs Nettle to use as garden ornaments. The chess game was finally ready to begin, when it was discovered that the only person in the village who knew all the rules was ill in bed with some badly inflamed wrinkles. Farmer Hale saved the day though. He sent a couple of his labourers back to his farm to gather up as many shotguns as they could find, then lined up the chess pieces against the wall of the old cobblers yard and we all took turns blasting them to matchwood. I thought it was terrific sport, but the carpenter got all sulky and sloped away muttering to himself.

As the afternoon turned to evening, the landlords of

the local inns arrived with barrels of scrumpo and beer, and everyone who made wine brought out bottles and bottles of the stuff. The nuns wheeled down a huge cartload they must have been saving for ages and started handing it out and swilling a good deal of it themselves, much to my surprise.

There was no food left, but it didn't seem to matter as most folk seemed quite content to drink heavily instead. It was a shame that all the decent musicians in the district had been booked to play elsewhere, and we had to make do with Mr Rubus' wind-up gramophone and his odd selection of records. As the evening went on things became more and more blurred I'm afraid, but I do remember dancing to that old classic '*My lovely Fay, I feel so gay*' with one of the younger nuns. That was the first time I'd ever kissed a girl and I never realised you had to use your tongue.

I'm sorry to say that's about the last thing I can remember, other than of being half-carried across the Green, and of waking up freezing cold in the allotments the next morning with a head that felt like it was stuffed full of suet. I'd lost my spotted neckerchief and all the buttons on my trousers were undone, but I felt strangely satisfied.

A PRESENT FOR THE KING

About a week after the Jubilee celebrations were over, the leader of the parish council decided we ought to show our appreciation by sending the King a present. A collection was taken around the village and the neighbouring farms, and the sum of two pounds, nine shillings and fourpence was raised. This wasn't a huge sum and was probably quite a bit less than was expected, but folk simply didn't have much spare cash in those days.

There were endless meetings to decide what to do with the money, but no agreement could be reached. This dragged on for month after month. Following one particularly heated discussion, at which three councillors ended up with black eyes, someone suggested that Mad Mr Mungo be commissioned to paint the King a picture.

The question then was the subject matter. I'd read that he liked Bognor, so I put the idea forward and was somewhat surprised when it was accepted. No-one had ever been to Bognor, but Mrs Nettle's sister's friend's cousin Beryl had retired to a caravan just along the coast from there, so Doc Grimm wrote to her and asked her for a postcard. Unfortunately when she finally got round to sending one it wasn't a great deal of use as we already knew what a donkey looked like.

To save any further delays, Mr Mungo reasoned that Bognor was probably similar to Lulworth Cove, but with a golden palace for the King to stay in, four long piers, a racetrack and some palm trees.

He finally started work on the painting towards the end of 1935 and completed it just after Christmas. It was given to Mr and Mrs Unwin to frame, and then sat around in the postman's house for a couple of weeks until he could be bothered to wrap it in brown paper and send it off to Sandringham. According to the postman, it would have arrived there on the morning of 20 January 1936, which sadly was the day the poor old King died. I do hope it cheered him up.

POCKET MONEY

Neither Tommy nor I ever had much money when we were nippers, so we were constantly looking for ways to make a few coppers. Penny for the Guy always worked well, as did Tommy pretending to be a dribbling lunatic with me shaking a tin mug at the summer fêtes. But these were few and far between, and since the collapse of our ingenious plan to steal vegetables out of peoples' gardens and then sell them back to them, things had been tough. It had been Tommy's fault for insisting that we 'mark our territory' and being caught squatting over Silas Nimrod's cucumber.

We finally realised we'd probably have to do some real work in order to get anywhere, so we made a sign that said 'Willing for a Shilling' and started wandering round the lanes looking hopeful. Some years later I told a rather upright military gentleman in a Rolls Royce towing a caravan about our little money-raising scheme when he saw me dib dib dibbing in a field, but that's another story.

Anyways, after a slow start of helping Widow Minger check her woolers for ticks, we did all sorts of stuff: we fetched bags of flour for Mrs Doodle, we dragged all the hassocks out of the church and beat the dust out of them, we swept out several cottages and we whitewashed walls, fences and most of our clothes. We even held down Mr Mungo's pet otter for him while he rubbed goose fat into its todders. It was meant to cure one of the spiteful thing's more disgusting habits, but I don't think it worked.

At the end of our labours we'd done quite well for ourselves, but we hadn't achieved our target sum. I can't remember how much it was, but we needed enough for Tommy to buy a smart new penknife he'd seen in the ironmonger's window, and for me to buy a pretty little butterfly bracelet for Millie Boule, who was a lovely young girl I was quite keen on. It was 1936, I'd just turned sixteen and I wanted to thrill her.

We decided to treat ourselves to a bag of sweets each, and it was while we were on our way to the village store that we met Mrs Nettle, who told us that her neighbour, Mrs Tucker, needed help as her rhododendron was out of control. This was a bit of a dilemma for us, as rumour had it that Mrs Tucker had poisoned at least two husbands and was probably a witch to boot. Since we needed the money we decided to go anyway, but as a precaution we borrowed Old Albert's little mongrel Woodrow to take along with us.

When we wandered into her garden, we found her laid out in the sunshine, wearing nothing but a large straw hat. I said I'd been told that her bush needed trimming, and she simply smiled at me, got up and wandered into her cottage. She then surprised us by returning to give Tommy some money just to go home. I ended up spending the whole of the afternoon with

Mrs Tucker, and she got me to do all sorts of things, none of which involved gardening. I don't know if she was a witch or not, but she certainly taught me a trick or two.

When I met Tommy the next day, we counted our coins again and found that we had enough for his penknife and the bracelet, which I put aside for Millie's birthday. And thanks to Mrs Tucker I was able to give her a pearl necklace as well.

NAUGHTY CHARLIE

Charlie Nettle was a good laugh and a bit of a practical joker when he was a lad. He'd probably deny it all now if he's still around, but I remember when he sneaked into blind Mrs Hobson's house and cut off all her hair while she was asleep. He wrote dirty words on her kitchen wall and moved all her furniture around so she didn't know where she was when she woke up. He would probably have gotten away with it if he hadn't taken one of her dead husband's waistcoats and worn it to church.

Charlie could spit a cherry stone through a partly open bedroom window, and loved chops and beans. He once climbed up and painted a giant gherkin and a couple of damsons on the roof of the Village Hall. At least I think that's what it was meant to be.

He caused a certain amount of bother when he turned all the signposts around and a long-awaited delivery of Marmite went missing, but he got his comeuppance when he pretended to collapse in the Square one day. A crowd gathered and Doc Grimm quickly stripped him to check for broken bones. Charlie leapt up to run home in his grubby pants, and everyone laughed because they had a huge hole in the back of them. We called him 'Cheeky Chas' after that.

Nearly everyone had a nickname back then. I don't really know why. Lily Titman's mother was known as The Lady because her cousin had once been to London and brought her back a lace handkerchief. Bumpy Fenner had dreadful boils on his face when he was a toddler, and Jumbo Carter claimed to have seen an elephant.

Fingers Crawford got his nickname when he was spotted trying to steal packets of biscuits from the bakery. I can't remember what Tugger Taylor was caught doing.

SLAUGHTER IN THE WOODS

My friendship with Mrs Tucker seemed to earn me a certain amount of respect around the village. Even Mr Guffer was impressed and asked me if I would care to join him for a pint in The Twitching Pig to discuss a business opportunity. Tommy was less enthusiastic and made up a rude rhyme about me which I still remember but won't repeat in full, although it was quite amusing I suppose. It began, 'His name's Cocque, her name's Tucker...' You can probably guess the rest yourself.

Anyways, that was how I found myself at the Inn one evening with a dented tankard of scrumpo and a bag of salty hoglumps to chew. The inside of the inn was a whole new world for me. I liked the poorly painted pictures of famous fish on the walls, the fat-spattered fireplace and the old men playing dominoes in a thick fog of cheap tobacco. I particularly enjoyed watching Fanny Muffet serving behind the bar in a blouse cut so low you could almost see her nublets. Fanny later left the village and married a Turkish merchant called Farook Batta, who'd made a fortune by inventing a new kind of cheroot especially for small children. He was a nice man by all accounts, but much to Fanny's consternation he wouldn't let her keep her maiden name.

Mr Guffer was the gamekeeper for the Baron's estate and he asked me if I could round up a number of youngsters to act as beaters and pickers-up at the weekend shoot. He said that if all went well there'd be good money in it for me and possibly another job afterwards.

I was at the head of a good crowd of helpers when we arrived at the Manor House early on a misty Saturday morning, where we were divided up, issued with flags and sticks, and instructed on what to do. Some time later the Baron and his cronies appeared, quite obviously the worse for wear after a heavy night of swilling from the Manor's vast wine cellar.

It was the Baron's first shoot, and as he couldn't cope with loud noises he had earplugs, earmuffs and a balaclava on beneath his deerstalker. Guffer did his best to explain the plan to him with a series of signs and gestures, but it didn't do any good. The Baron and his friends wandered off with their various servants and loaders, and formed an unsteady line by the edge of a wood. A beautiful falcon then chose a fateful moment to glide over. Someone pointed at it and the Baron immediately shot it out of the sky. Game took flight from all directions at once and there was total mayhem as the Baron's friends blazed away at anything that moved. There was no beating or picking-up; we all hit the ground and stayed as low as we could while bags and bags of cartridges were discharged. Guffer said Waterloo must have sounded like that, but I've never been to a big station so I wouldn't know.

When the ammunition finally ran out, we surveyed

the damage while the Baron's party wandered off for lunch. There were dead birds and animals everywhere, and we could hear sobbing from the long grass. It turned out to be one of the Baron's sullen servants, who was uninjured but from the smell of him had been very frightened indeed.

Mr Guffer let the village youngsters take most of the recently deceased wildlife home with them, although a good deal of it had been shot at such close range it was hard to tell what it was. I stayed and helped him bury two retrievers, several cats and the Baroness's prize pony, which had been in the wrong place at the wrong time.

On the way home that night I had a pocketful of coins and a couple of plump pheasants, so I popped in to see Mrs Tucker and gave her one. She was very grateful.

MARKET DAY

Every few months, most of the village went on an expedition in an assortment of carts and wagons to the county town for the big market. It was an opportunity to buy all sorts of wondrous goods that we would otherwise never have seen, and to sell produce, crafts and anything else of value that was lying around. On one such occasion I hitched a ride on Widow Minger's cart with my mate Tommy and some of the nuns.

On this trip, Tommy was hoping to take orders for his new scarecrow. It had taken him months to build, and it could wave its arms and legs and even spin its head round and round. I thought it unlikely to do well because although it was very efficient at bird-scaring, it worked by a complex series of cables and linkages that required a full-time operator.

I had plenty of animal pelts to sell now that I was a regular helper in Mr Guffer's various activities, and Mrs Tucker had asked me to keep a sharp eye out for shiny red ribbon for her sister's birthday. I had to keep it quiet as she didn't want her sister to know, and luckily I managed to find some and slip her a length later that night.

We arrived at the market early to get good pitches, and worked hard to get our stalls set up as quickly as possible. Unfortunately Mrs Nettle's big salad display collapsed under the weight of her oversized tomatoes, which rolled everywhere and caused a number of minor injuries. Widow Minger failed to sell any of her revolting pies, until someone suggested she change the labels on them from 'Crudlumps' to 'Dorset Specials'. That did the trick. Mad Mr Mungo had a collection of garish paintings he'd dashed off depicting judges, peasants, beatings and hangings, which went down very well with the town's better-off inhabitants, and Tommy's sister Elsie made a few bob from her edible smalls woven from strips of celery. Mrs Doodle's buns were massive and very popular indeed.

Anyways, I'd sold all my wares early on to a creepy handbag dealer with a damp handshake, so I had time to wander round the rest of the market. I headed for the livestock auction on the far side of the field, where an immense bad-tempered bull was being restrained with some difficulty by several herdsmen. As I approached, Old Albert spotted me, waved, and by doing so placed the final bid. There was then a rumpus as he argued with the angry auctioneer and swore at his assistants, eventually threatening them by whirling a large onion in a string bag round his head. He was easily overpowered as he was rolling drunk, but as he was led away he suddenly heaved the contents of his stomach down the auctioneer's Wellington boots.

I moved swiftly on to the bric-a-brac stalls and Mrs Nettle sidled up to me to ask if I would buy something for her and sneak it back to the village. For some reason she was too nervous to make the purchase herself. That was how I ended up with a small glass rolling pin pushed down the front of my breeches.

When I met up with the rest of the villagers later, I found them in a state of excitement; Widow Minger had received a marriage proposal, and a scruffy man from Poole had very nearly bought Tommy's scarecrow, but had been distracted at the last minute when his goat fainted.

I had an uncomfortable journey home as the rolling pin was tight against my leg, but the nuns smiled and winked at me all the way.

MR PERKS

Perhaps I ought to tell you the strange tale of Mr Perks. He was a sort of odd-job man who mostly helped the old folk with gardening, small repairs and knob polishing. One morning, he pulled up a tree root which came free suddenly and banged his head on the ground when he fell over. He went back to his little house and never came out of his bedroom again.

His poor sister passed food to him through a flap he cut in the door and emptied his bucket once a week. When he died some years later, they found him surrounded by stacks of ledgers in which he'd written the word 'bastard' over fifty thousand times.

A TRIP TO THE SEASIDE

Most of the villagers never strayed far from home, but now and again a day trip was organised and I was always keen to see more of the world. I went to all the markets if I could get a lift; I'd helped deliver a ram to an angry woman near Plush; I'd been to see Lloyd George at Tolpuddle, and I'd even spent a day with some of the nuns at Cerne Abbas, where they sat all agog and stared at the hillside for hours on end.

When the chance came for a trip to the seaside at Swanage, I jumped at it. It was the summer of 1937 and the weather was beautiful. Unfortunately, Tommy couldn't come on the trip as his grandma thought he'd deliberately fallen on her hollyhocks and he wasn't allowed out, but Millie was eager.

Our small party caught the early train from Dorchester and I enjoyed the ride very much, despite Mrs Nettle constantly complaining that we were going too fast, and Silas Nimrod crunching endless pickled onions from a jar he'd jammed into his coat pocket.

When we arrived at Swanage Railway Station me and Millie headed straight for the beach, where we scoffed fish and chips while marvelling at all the people on the sands and laughing at the young children falling off donkeys. It was a lovely day and we were desperate to get in the sea. Millie's mother had made her a swimsuit out of some thin flowery curtains, which turned transparent as soon as it got wet. I wanted to stay in the water all day.

In the afternoon we wandered past the pier and watched a couple of local fishermen cheating some visiting toffs out of their money by selling them old crab shells packed with mashed potato. We bumped into Reverend Toucher who told us he'd been to see a giant globe, which seemed a bit unlikely, and spotted Old Albert who'd fallen asleep on a bench halfway through eating a sardine sandwich and was covered in seagulls. We hired a rowing boat and I struggled to get us about halfway across the bay, where I called a friendly greeting to a ruddy-faced man hauling up lobster pots. He yelled at me to sod off out of it and take my blonde tart with me, which I did as I suppose he must have owned the sea.

It was very nearly time to catch the train home, so we quickly rowed back to shore and visited a number of the shops to find souvenirs. Millie bought a small bag of polished seashells and I settled for a stick of pink rock and ten Capstan Full Strength.

When we met the other villagers back at the station, we found that a couple of the labourers had spent the whole of their visit in the pub and were barely conscious. One of them had a fat lip but couldn't remember how he got it, while another was wearing somebody else's trousers back-to-front and smelt strongly of fish. He insisted on standing up all the way home.

The train was delayed while a robber with a suitcase full of stolen marmalade was chased down the line at Corfe, and it was very late by the time we finally got back to the village. I remember feeling tired but happy after a wonderful day out, and drifting off to sleep thinking of Millie and knowing I'd be stiff in the morning.

WEDDING BELLS

Everyone loves a good wedding and although I don't recall many taking place, when Mr Guffer finally got round to marrying Bessie Goodbust practically the whole village turned out. Of course they already had three small children with another on the way, but that didn't really bother anyone back then.

Bessie's family weren't very well off, so they couldn't afford to buy her a dress. They persuaded the undertaker to let them have some of the cloth he used for shrouds, and printed tiny shapes onto it using carefully carved potato halves and watered-down ink. Tommy's grandma actually sewed the dress together by hand and I have to say she made a pretty good job of it, although she moaned about how much cotton she was using and went on and on about her missing sewing machine. I happened to know that Tommy had swapped it for a box of Meccano and a spare rubber ear from a Swiss automaton over a year earlier, but I kept quiet. Tommy had hoped to wear the ear on special occasions, but sadly it was the wrong one.

On the morning of the wedding, the good women of the village decorated the church with masses of flowers from their own gardens and the surrounding meadows. At first, there was bit of a row as Reverend Toucher had raging hay fever and was sneezing violently. He didn't want the flowers inside as he was worried he wouldn't be able to conduct the service. Someone suggested he tie a handkerchief soaked in vinegar around his nose, and that seemed to work a treat, although his voice did sound a bit odd.

The only person who wasn't welcome at the wedding was Bessie's cousin Tessie. They'd fallen out over a damaged teaspoon and wouldn't speak to each other. Happily, Bessie was talked round by her mother, and Tessie was allowed to stand outside on a stepladder and watch the service through one of the windows.

At midday, we all piled into church and I was impressed by how much effort everyone had made to smarten themselves up. Mickey the Bug had washed his red smock and had a new blue cap which made him look a bit like a gnome, Fanny Muffet was almost wearing a thin pink frock, and Mad Mr Mungo had tied a ribbon round his withered arm. The Baron and Baroness arrived, much to our surprise, and took their place at the front in their reserved pews which were the only ones that had cushions. The Baron was in his full dress uniform that was covered in medals he didn't deserve, and the Baroness screwed up her face as though she had a bad smell under her nose.

Mr Guffer and his best man were stood at the front by the altar looking nervous for quite a few minutes, until all of a sudden the organist started to play and Bessie walked slowly through the big studded oak doors. She looked radiant with fresh daisies in her hair and each of her children carrying a small bunch of baby carrots. As Bessie's father was long dead, she was to be given away by her uncle Digby from Portland, who was an old salt who'd lost both his legs on a trawler. His Bath chair was unfortunately damaged by a rut on the way to the church, but the greengrocer kindly stepped in at the last minute and wheeled him up the aisle in his barrow.

The service went very well indeed, although there was some tittering when the Reverend addressed the bridegroom by his full name of Gerald Albonius Wobbleigh Guffer, and Old Albert thought it hilarious when he suggested to the newly-married couple that if they ever had an argument they should stop and touch each other's ring. There weren't even any objections to the marriage, unlike the time when Silas Nimrod had to overpower an enraged charlady armed with a breadknife and knuckle dusters, but that's another story.

There was a great cheer when Guffer kissed his new bride, and we all followed them outside where the Baron's Bentley was parked on the lawn, guarded by his chauffeur and his butler. The Baron shook Guffer's hand and passed him an envelope, got straight into the back of his car and was driven away without a backward glance.

Due to a misunderstanding, the Village Hall had been booked for the day by a group of trainee mime artists from a nearby hamlet, so the reception was held at the Twitching Pig. It was one of the few big occasions where there was absolutely no trouble at all, other than a certain amount of laughter when Fanny Muffet's mother noticed a group of men taking a little too much interest in her scantily-clad daughter. She jumped up onto one of the tables and said in a very loud voice, 'Will you men please stop staring at my Fanny.'

Mrs Doodle had made a wonderful wedding cake in the shape of a fox's head, in honour of Guffer's position as gamekeeper, and while the speeches were being made a number of us went outside to decorate the cart that would take the happy couple and their children away. We had lots of old tin cans which we tied on with string, and the butcher produced a horse's donger which he tastefully hung from the back.

All too soon the wedding was over, and as a smiling Guffer was climbing into the cart someone asked him what was in the envelope the Baron had given him. He'd forgotten about it in the excitement, so he pulled it out of his pocket and opened it there and then. I think we all hoped it would be one of those white five pound notes we'd heard about, but it turned out to be a letter giving him a week's notice. It was only a month or so later that the Baron's Bentley mysteriously caught fire, but I'm sure it was just a coincidence.

LUCKY EGGY

I must tell you about Eggy Dill. I'm not sure what his real name was now, it might have been Donald. Or maybe Thaddeus. He owned quite a large property at the bottom of Sluttern Passage, just past the Tossing Tree; which was so called because for some reason people used to toss old socks up into the branches. It was meant to bring good luck I think. One particularly cold winter I recall Old Albert knocking some socks down with a long pole and burning them to keep warm. He probably should have worn them.

Eggy was the only person in the village who encouraged outsiders, as he set up a kind of holiday home in the back of his house. It was the part his elderly mother and aunt had used until they both died after getting a bit befuddled and making a toadstool and dropwort omelette. Eggy didn't discover them for weeks, and then buried them himself somewhere out in the woods. When PC Stodge found out he went round to ask Eggy what the hell he thought he was playing at, but Eggy managed to get him drunk and nothing more was said.

Eggy needed money as his collar-stiffening business was failing badly, so he put an advertisement in one of the big London newspapers for anyone who wanted to enjoy the true heart of Dorset. He got quite a few replies, and guests started to turn up a couple of months later. The first few were put off a bit as Eggy hadn't bothered to do any cleaning, and the whole place reeked of vomit. His mother's moth-eaten clothes were still in the wardrobe and he hadn't even moved his dead aunt's shoes, which were still under the table where she'd gone nose-down. I don't think they liked the look of the house much either, as it was painted entirely in grey; walls, ceilings, doors, the lot. This was because Eggy's uncle had been in charge of the stores for HMS Codpiece, a Scone class cruiser that ran aground during its sea trials after the nature-loving but boss-eyed captain attempted to get a better view of some puffins. There was also a life-sized wooden statue of Florence Nightingale leant up against Eggy's front porch, but where that came from I have no idea.

Anyways, Eggy found out that London folk expect a bit of privacy too. When a young professional couple filled the tin bath one evening, Eggy heard them and walked in to ask if he could use the water afterwards. It might have been all right, but he was stark naked and the girl's screams could be heard for some distance. Eggy went through every guest's belongings while they were out, and was often caught wearing some of their clothes when they came back. He made quite a few pounds though, as nearly everyone paid in full but left early.

As usual, everything worked out well for Eggy. A very rich widow who came down for a few weeks to recover from the loss of her husband, was delighted when she returned from a walk to find Eggy sat in her motor car pretending to drive it and honking the horn. He was dressed in her flimsy undergarments with her best hat perched at a jaunty angle on his lap. Apparently she reached in, lifted the hat and he just giggled. They left together the next morning and I didn't see him again for years, until I thought I spotted him slapping a beggar outside a Bournemouth betting shop.

KIT KAT

Mrs Doodle was the first person in our village to eat a Kit Kat Chocolate Crisp. Her husband bought it for her in a shop in Sherborne and, needless to say, it caused a great deal of excitement. A special gathering at the Village Hall was arranged so that everyone could witness the opening, and Mrs Doodle was presented with a special commemorative headscarf. Very few ordinary folk like us owned a camera in those days, so people took notes for their diaries and the empty wrapper was framed and tacked up on the wall, where it remained until it was destroyed in the great silage eruption of 1949.

When I finally started to earn decent money I would often buy a Kit Kat and share it with Millie, as she loved it when I gave her a couple of fingers.

DARTS

Did I mention that our village had a darts team? Most of the players were more interested in drinking than actually winning the game, but I used to go along and watch whenever they were playing at home, as it was always a good night out. The games were held in The Twitching Pig and the landlord, Fats Tanner, was the captain. He was completely useless and folk used to say that he couldn't hit a haystack with a mutton-brush, but it was his inn so he always played, even though he never won a single game as he only had two darts to everyone else's three. He'd lost the other one at a pub in Wareham, when a shockingly wild throw had hit someone's dog just below the tail and caused a massive punch-up. I think that was the same night Casper Brown claimed to have seen a black bear on a roof, but he'd probably had one too many.

Come to think of it, nearly every game seemed to end in a disagreement. Sometimes it was a row over the scoring, as I don't think any of our team could add up, let alone take away, but usually it was down to Gob and Nob, two of the local farmhands. They were an odd pair. They once decided that they could only speak to each other by belching the words, and on another occasion they spent the whole evening kicking each other up the arse and yelping like puppies. Visiting teams didn't know what to make of them, and claimed to be put off by Gob shouting 'What's that then?' after every throw as he could barely see the board, and by Nob constantly getting in the way, apologising, then doing it again and again.

The best match I ever saw was in 1938 when we played a team from The Five Middens. Or it might have been The Golden Vole. Anyways, it was a close-run thing and there was real tension in the air when it came to the last game with the scores level. Judson Phatt, who was probably our best player, was up against a big bearded chap who made a bit more room for himself by smashing a beer mug on the edge of a table and waving it in the face of anyone who got too close.

I don't recall exactly what happened in that final game, but I do know that Judson won it and the whole place went mad. Backs were slapped, huge numbers of drinks were consumed and many men stripped to their underpants. The other team took their defeat well, or so we all thought at the time. It wasn't until the following morning that the inn's sign was found tied to a cow which was wandering about in the lane and was heavily smeared in what appeared to be mud, but unfortunately wasn't.

THE GRUBBS

Sometimes when I have a cup of milky tea, I'm reminded of Bertha Grubb. She was a milkmaid when I was a young man and a lot of people were a bit scared of her. She must have been about five foot six so she towered over the other girls, and she was quite a character. I remember when me and Tommy were having a whizzing contest behind the stables one day, she saw us, dropped to her haunches and beat us by at least a yard.

She had rosy cheeks, long plaits and tremendous thighs. She never had very much to say for herself, but most folks were wary of her because she had such a dreadful temper. She was strong too. When one of the cows kicked her pail over early one morning, she stood up and punched it on the side of the head so hard that it collapsed in a heap. I quite liked her, and I think she quite liked me too. Mind you, I never called her names like some of the others did, and at the right time of year I would always try and find her at lunchtime and let her have a taste of my plums.

Bertha lived in a collection of rickety buildings with a lovely view past the crooked oak and over the old plague pit. She had loads of brothers, sisters and cousins, but back then most families were pretty big. I don't know if it was to make sure there were always plenty of workers or because there wasn't much to do in the evenings.

The Grubb family was well known all around the district as a thieving and unpleasant bunch, and PC Stodge spent many a day searching round their place for anything that had turned up missing. He once found one of the headlights from the Baron's Bentley under a patchwork eiderdown in the Grubbs' outhouse, but they said they had no idea how it got there. The Grubbs would shout and curse at anyone who went too close to their property, and would swipe anything that wasn't nailed down. I think they came from Bere Regis. They stole flowers from the churchyard, wood from the coffin-maker, sacks of grain and countless chickens. They caused Farmer Hale no end of pain, especially after they pinched his cock.

Two of Betha's aunties lived there too and we called them Fish and Fowl. Fish had a kind of down-turned mouth with tiny sharp teeth like a pike, and Fowl stank. They made lovely jam though.

I once got invited to a party at Bertha's, to celebrate Billy Grubb's release from prison. He'd been banged up for nearly three years for exposing himself to a nervous thatcher, who'd fallen off his ladder and badly bruised his undercarriage. That might sound a long sentence for a fourteen year old, but it was the latest in a long list of offences that ranged from soiling gravestones to releasing an angry polecat in the tripe tent at the annual Knitwear and Bucket Spectacular.

Billy was not one of my favourite people. He tied

bangers to cats' tails, he waited outside school to bully the smaller children and would run off with the ball if we started a game of cricket on the Green. Me and Mr Guffer got rid of him though. He accused Billy of taking his pocket watch and PC Stodge discovered it in one of his spare hobnail boots, hidden under his bed - which was just where I'd planted it during the party, when there was a lull between the slug racing and the bare knuckle fight. Billy did six hard years for that, but I never felt the slightest bit guilty about it; even when I heard he'd had to 'marry' a burly armed robber in the prison scullery.

Bertha moved into one of the tithe cottages with Skinny Len, a farmhand who must have been twice her age and half her size. He always looked dead on his feet and I remember asking Bertha whether he was ill. She told me he was fine, and that she fed him plenty of watercress to 'Keep him hard and save on lard.' They ended up with five children, three dogs and Auntie Fish.

MAVIS MONK

Oh yes, I remember the time when Mavis Monk claimed that an evil green hedgepig was sitting on her front lawn and staring at her, so she had to climb over her back fence to collect her milk. It turned out to be a lump of mud with grass growing on it. She then claimed that a man was sticking his wilbur through her letterbox late at night. Sadly, this turned out to be true as Doc Grimm had a bizarre sense of humour.

Mavis was a tiny bird-like woman who was nervous of just about everything, and twittered away to herself as she scurried to and from the Mill, where she was employed as a spindle tapper. If someone upset her she would leave a note for them pinned to their front gate, but since she couldn't write more than a few letters, the notes were mostly scribble. I never saw her eat anything, even at Reverend Toucher's 'Soup and Saviour' evenings, but she craftily swigged sloe gin from a silver flask she kept in her handbag.

Tommy's sister told me that Mavis stopped the Doc's little game by crouching behind her front door with a cupful of bleach and a small potted cactus.

Mavis kept scores of zebra finches in a large aviary at the back of her neat little cottage in Butt Row. Where she got them from I have no idea. She was a crack shot with a catapult, which she used to discourage the local cats. On summer weekends she would sit in an old deck chair inside the aviary all day looking at picture books, before emerging in the evening covered in droppings.

Some of her neighbours hated the constant beeping noise the finches made, and I know that they paid Old Albert a few coppers to sneak into her garden with some poisoned millet. Mavis took his hat clean off with a ball bearing from her kitchen window, so everyone let her be after that.

AN UNUSUAL VISIT

Letters were a rare treat in my youth, so I remember I was more than a little excited when I found an envelope with my name on it stuffed into the pocket of my dungarees early one autumn morning. I was doing a bit of work for a local builder at the time, and I sat and read it on my break while the other lads were arguing over exactly what 'Peace for our time' was supposed to mean.

It wasn't a love letter as I'd hoped, and was very poorly written, but it seemed to be an invitation to visit my long-lost great uncle Gideon, who had recently bought a cottage near Silliborne Nutter and was anxious to meet up. I couldn't fully make out the address and I had no idea how the letter had reached me, but I was intrigued and decided to head over there at the weekend.

On the Saturday, I wandered round to Ernie Snook's house and asked him if I could borrow his motorcycle. I think it was a BSA Blue Czar, and his father had bought it for him as a reward for not selling the photographs he'd taken of his sister. For once Ernie agreed straight away and didn't even ask for petrol money, so I rode off to Millie's to see if she wanted to come with me. I didn't have a license just then, but as long as you didn't do anything stupid no-one really cared. As I waited for Millie to persuade her mother, Doc Grimm saw me and ran off down the lane. He returned a couple of minutes later with a flying helmet which he said I ought to wear. He told me it had once belonged to Manfred Von Richtofen, but I doubt that was true. It wasn't even red.

Anyways, we set off quite happily, found our way to Silliborne and parked the motorcycle near an abandoned seed drill with a yapping dog tied to it. As I didn't have a proper address, I decided to ask someone, so I went into a funny little shop that seemed to sell everything from slips to sausages. A pleasant round-faced lady with a scar across her nose thought she knew who I was looking for, came to the front door of the shop and pointed down an overgrown path past a little chapel. Millie didn't fancy the idea of scratching her legs on the brambles, so she bought a copy of *Ladles for Ladies* and settled herself down on a grass bank to read it.

I made my way down the path, and approaching a slightly run-down cottage I spotted a wizened white-haired man sat outside on an upturned pail, smoking a clay pipe and picking his feet with a screwdriver. I asked him if he was Gideon and he nodded and beckoned me inside. The moment I sat down he said, 'You'll be wanting tea, do you?' I politely declined, and there then followed a couple of the weirdest hours of my life. He told me he had next to no furniture as he'd lost it in a dice game on the boat over from Ireland, where he'd been living for forty years or so. He then rattled on and on about scores of people I'd never heard of, places I'd never been, and alternative names for figs. Every few minutes he'd stop and say, 'You'll be wanting tea now then, do you?' It nearly drove me mad, so in the end I gave in and said, 'Yes please, that would be very nice.' He completely ignored me and never made any tea.

I hardly got a word in edgeways, but I did mention that I liked the glass swan he had on his mantelpiece, and he nodded thoughtfully. When he finally ran out of steam, I said I'd better be wending my way and he asked for an address so he could send me the swan when he'd finished with it. I remember thinking that was strange, so I gave him the address of the Twitching Pig.

When I found Millie she had dozed off, so I gave her a gentle poke. We then got back on Ernie's motorcycle and set off again. The roads weren't very good in those days, and about half way back something came loose at the back that caused Millie's seat to vibrate something rotten. Arriving at her house I apologised for the ride home, but she had a dreamy look on her face and said she'd didn't mind a bit.

I returned the motorcycle to Ernie's, but he wasn't about so I left it and headed for the Inn. Ernie, Charlie and Tommy burst out laughing as soon as they saw me, and when they calmed down I discovered that they'd written and planted the letter from great uncle Gideon as a joke. I admitted they'd got me good and proper, and started to wonder who on earth I'd visited that afternoon.

A month or so later a package with my name on it was delivered to the Twitching Pig with the glass swan in it. My mates thought this was even funnier and kept on and on about it for the next year or so. Right up until the day Gideon died and left me his cottage.

CLEVER TOMMY

You've probably noticed that I spent a lot of time with my mate Tommy as I was growing up, and he was a good friend to me. He was a clever little so-and-so too. He was always trying to make new inventions and the like, some of which actually worked for a while. I remember he rigged up a series of mirrors for big Mrs Doodle so that she could see to shave the back of her knees, and when the village finally got electricity he somehow managed to run a cable from Ernie Snook's house to his mother's to get it for nothing. I don't think the Snooks ever caught on. He sold a few of his less complicated scarecrows, and so far as I know his sod detector is still in use today.

Not all of his ideas were quite so successful though. He built a whole series of traps which he put in the woods, but all he caught was Judson Phatt's bad leg when he sneaked up there with a filthy magazine. He also spent months working on a peculiar kind of mechanical dog, but gave up when it bit him. His toad battery was weak and ineffective, and his mud cannon didn't seem to serve any useful purpose at all.

He was always quite a calm lad, and he lied for me on lots of occasions when I was spending time somewhere I probably shouldn't have been. This was mostly when I was seeing Millie, but taking more than a passing interest in Lily Titman too. Oh, and Mrs Tucker now and again. And the lady over at the new garage by the crossroads. And the young nun with the vestigial tail.

I didn't see quite so much of Tommy after he got a job at an engineering firm near Kittwhistle, but we'd always try and meet up at weekends for a drink, and to see if he was ever going to beat me at arm wrestling. I don't think he ever did, but I do recall that he won the raw egg swallowing contest that made me and Charlie sick as a pigs, and made Ernie cry like a baby girl.

Tommy was a good lad, so I'm not going to tell you the story about the plumbing spares and the liver. Not this time, anyway.

HERE WE GO

They say that folks can remember where they were when they heard important news. I know that most of the villagers heard that Mr Chamberlain had declared war when Reverend Toucher announced it at the end of his evening service, after the notices about bible study and whose turn it was to take pancakes to the Asylum. This was 1939 of course. Some of the older folk were very shocked as they hadn't realised the previous war had ended. I thought this was a bit odd but when I went to look at the War Memorial in the Square, I found that the stone mason had forgotten to add 1918 to the inscription. There were only two names on the Memorial; Abraham Greener, who had choked to death on a Belgian bun before he even reached the trenches, and William Clod who had never returned from the front, but strong rumour had it that he'd run off with a pretty young Frenchman called Alphonse.

As soon as the news spread, doddery old Mr Faff, a retired pigswill inspector, grabbed a pitchfork from a neighbour's lean-to and ran to stand guard outside the Mullers' cottage. He stood there every day from dawn till dusk for months on end, until someone let slip that the Muller family had moved away years ago. He then took it upon himself to sit by the side of the lane and demand to see the 'papers' of anyone who happened to pass by. Since he couldn't read, we all ended up carrying around pages torn out of Mrs Beeton's Cookbook. My page showed how to make a lemon flan.

Anyways, the village ladies were all disappointed to think that the soldiers from the camp would no doubt be moving on, and Tommy's mother and sister seemed to be particularly upset. They didn't even join in when the rest of the village went on a mass campaign of stockpiling food. Every last tin, bottle, jar and can was found and filled with anything that could be preserved, and then hidden away in the most unlikely places and forgotten. I heard that several large cans of sparrows were discovered up a chimney just a few years ago.

Other than that, things were pretty quiet for some time and me, Tommy, and a few of the other older lads started to talk about volunteering for the army. We knew we were unlikely to be called up, as our names didn't appear on any Government lists. Any mail that looked official had always been quietly destroyed by the postman, who'd got it into his head that it was his job to decide who received what. He kept back parcels if people had been rude to him and read anything that looked personal, sometimes adding his own notes on the end of the letters in brown crayon.

In the end, it was only me, Tommy, Charlie Nettle and Ernie Snook who set off to find a recruitment office one Saturday lunchtime. We would have left earlier, but Charlie thought he might not be tall enough and had spent the morning nailing bits of wood to the bottom of his boots.

We caught the bus to Dorchester and were directed to a church hall where a very smart soldier with several stripes on his arm and a cap with the peak down over his eyes stood to attention outside. As we approached, Charlie got nervous and threw up down the front of his waistcoat, and Ernie chose that moment to turn tail and run. We suspected he would as he was a cowardly little git, so it was just the three of us who were ushered in and asked our names and ages. We were then sent off in turn for a medical and I went last. The only thing I can really remember about it is that the doctor had very cold hands and looked a bit like Oliver Hardy.

When I got back to the main room, I found I was the only one there. Tommy and Charlie had been rejected; Tommy because of his missing ear, and Charlie because it turned out he was colour-blind, had flat feet, poor hearing, tunnel vision and couldn't tell his left from his right. Otherwise he would have been A1.

I signed a stack of forms, was given a cigarette and a voucher for a meat pie, shook hands with the sergeant and asked him if I was in the army yet. He leaned down and grinned at me, grabbed the front of my jacket, lifted me clean off my feet and said quietly, 'That's Reet Boy!'

SEE YOU NEXT TIME

Anyways, there you have it. These are some of the things that happened to me as I grew into a young man. There were lots of other goings on, such as the time the Baron led the Hunt right through the Morris Dancing Regional Finals, and the only recorded fatality at a Dorset skittles match, but they're for another day.

And maybe I'll tell you about my disastrous spell in the army, what happened when the American GIs came to the village, and how Tommy ended up with a medal and two wives.

We'll see.